THE HOBBIT

or
There and Back Again

by
J. R. R. Tolkien

Adapted by
Charles Dixon

Illustrated by
David Wenzel

Eclipse Books

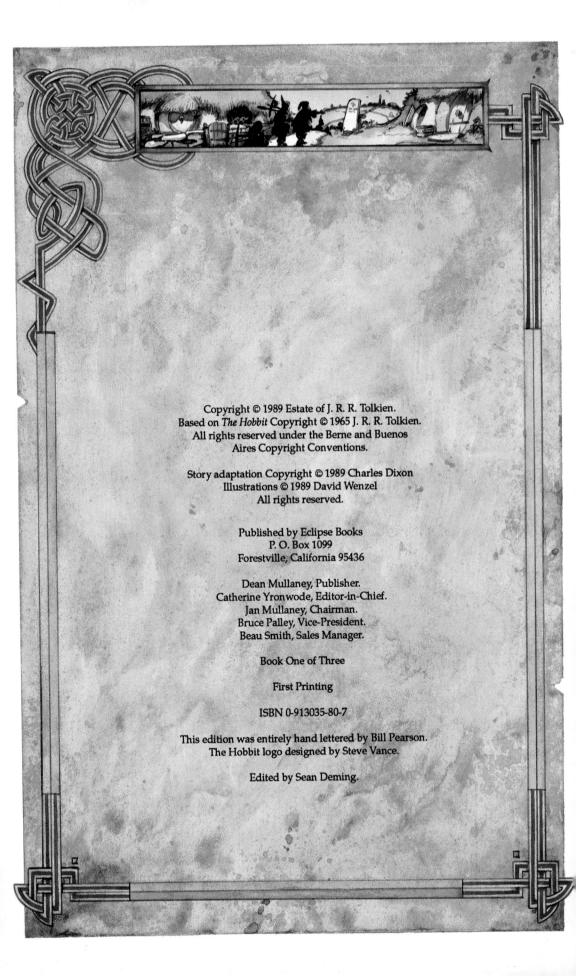

Published by Eclipse Books
P. O. Box 1099
Forestville, California 95436

Dean Mullaney, Publisher.
Catherine Yronwode, Editor-in-Chief.
Jan Mullaney, Chairman.
Bruce Palley, Vice-President.
Beau Smith, Sales Manager.

Book One of Three

First Printing

ISBN 0-913035-80-7

This edition was entirely hand lettered by Bill Pearson.
The Hobbit logo designed by Steve Vance.

Edited by Sean Deming.

In a hole in the ground there lived a hobbit. Not a nasty, dirty, wet hole, nor yet a dry, bare sand hole: it was a hobbit hole, and that means comfort.

This hobbit's hole was on The Hill, as all the people for many miles around called it, and his name was Baggins.

People considered the Bagginses very respectable, not only because most of them were rich, but also because they never had any adventures or did anything unexpected.

This is a story of how a Baggins had an adventure, and found himself doing and saying things altogether unexpected.

What is a hobbit?

I suppose hobbits need some description nowadays, since they have become rare and shy of the Big People, as they call us.

They are a little people, smaller than dwarves. They are inclined to be fat in the stomach; they dress in bright colors and wear no shoes, because their feet grow natural leathery soles and thick warm brown hair.

The mother of this particular hobbit — of Bilbo Baggins, that is — was the famous Belladonna Took! Once in a while members of the Took-clan would go and have adventures. They discreetly disappeared, and the family hushed it up; the Tooks were not as respectable as the Bagginses.

It is probable that Bilbo, Belladonna's only son, although he looked and behaved like his **father**, got something a bit queer in his make-up from the Took side, something that only waited for a chance to come out.

Oh.

1

WHAT ON *EARTH* DID I ASK HIM TO TEA FOR?!

Heh Heh Heh Heh

SKRHITCH SKRITCH

When tea-time came the next day, Bilbo had almost forgotten about Gandalf.

GOOD GRACIOUS ME! *GANDALF!*

DING-A-DING

DING-A-DING

DING-A-DING

I AM SO SORRY TO KEEP YOU—

—OH!

7

8

WE ARE MET TO DISCUSS OUR PLANS, OUR WAYS, MEANS, POLICY AND DEVICES. WE SHALL SOON BEFORE THE BREAK OF DAY START ON OUR LONG JOURNEY...

...A JOURNEY FROM WHICH SOME OF US MAY NEVER RETURN.

MAY NEVER RETURN?!

WE HAVE LOST OUR HOST, I FEAR.

HUMPH! WILL HE DO, DO YOU THINK? AS SOON AS I CLAPPED EYES ON THE LITTLE FELLOW, I HAD MY DOUBTS.

HE LOOKS MORE LIKE A GROCER THAN A BURGLAR!

PARDON ME, DID YOU SAY "BURGLAR"?

YES. I WAS TALKING ABOUT YOU. GANDALF TOLD US THAT THERE WAS A BURGLAR IN THESE PARTS LOOKING FOR A JOB AT ONCE, AND THAT HE HAD ARRANGED FOR A MEETING HERE THIS WEDNESDAY TEA-TIME.

THERE IS THE MARK ON YOUR DOOR— THE USUAL ONE IN THE TRADE, OR USED TO BE— BURGLAR WANTS A GOOD JOB, PLENTY OF EXCITEMENT AND REASONABLE REWARD.

BURGLAR?

YOU CAN SAY EXPERT TREASURE HUNTER IF YOU LIKE. IT'S ALL THE SAME TO US.

LET'S HAVE NO MORE ARGUMENT. IF I SAY MISTER BAGGINS IS A BURGLAR, A BURGLAR HE IS, OR WILL BE WHEN THE TIME COMES. THERE IS A LOT MORE IN HIM THAN YOU GUESS, AND A DEAL MORE THAN HE HAS ANY IDEA OF HIMSELF.

NOW, BILBO, MY BOY, FETCH THE LAMP, AND LET'S HAVE A LITTLE LIGHT ON...

9

...THIS!

THIS MAP WAS MADE BY THROR, YOUR GRANDFATHER, THORIN. IT IS A PLAN OF THE *MOUNTAIN* WHERE THE DRAGON SMAUG HAS PILED UP ALL YOUR ANCESTORS' WEALTH, AND SLEEPS ON IT FOR A BED.

THERE IS A DRAGON MARKED IN RED ON THE MOUNTAIN, BUT IT WILL BE EASY ENOUGH TO FIND HIM WITHOUT THAT, IF EVER WE ARRIVE THERE.

THIS HAND POINTS TO A RUNE THAT MARKS A SECRET ENTRANCE, A HIDDEN PASSAGE TO THE LOWER HALLS.

LOOK AT THE MAP AT THE END OF THIS BOOK

IT MAY HAVE BEEN SECRET ONCE, BUT HOW DO WE KNOW THAT IT IS SECRET ANY LONGER?

OLD SMAUG HAS LIVED THERE LONG ENOUGH NOW TO FIND OUT ANYTHING THERE IS TO KNOW ABOUT THOSE CAVES.

HE MAY— BUT HE CAN'T HAVE *USED* IT FOR YEARS AND YEARS. IT IS TOO *SMALL!*

"FIVE FEET HIGH THE DOOR AND THREE MAY WALK ABREAST," SAY THE RUNES, BUT SMAUG COULD NOT CREEP INTO A HOLE THAT SIZE, CERTAINLY NOT AFTER DEVOURING SO MANY OF THE DWARVES AND MEN OF DALE.

IT SEEMS A GREAT BIG HOLE TO ME. HOW COULD SUCH A LARGE DOOR BE KEPT SECRET?

I SHOULD GUESS IT IS A CLOSED DOOR WHICH HAS BEEN MADE TO LOOK EXACTLY LIKE THE SIDE OF THE MOUNTAIN.

ALSO, WITH THE MAP WENT A KEY, A SMALL AND CURIOUS KEY. HERE IT IS, THORIN— YOU MUST KEEP IT SAFE!

IN-DEED I WILL! NOW, SUPPOSING THE BURGLAR-EXPERT GIVES US SOME IDEAS OR SUGGES-TIONS.

FIRST I SHOULD LIKE TO KNOW A BIT MORE ABOUT THINGS. I MEAN ABOUT THE GOLD AND THE DRAGON, AND ALL THAT, AND HOW IT GOT THERE, AND WHO IT BELONGS TO, AND SO ON AND FURTHER.

The next morning when he awoke, Bilbo was really relieved to find the dwarves had all gone on without him; and yet in a way he could not help feeling just a trifle disappointed. The feeling surprised him.

DON'T BE A FOOL, BILBO BAGGINS! THINKING OF DRAGONS AND ALL THAT OUTLANDISH NONSENSE AT YOUR AGE!

MY DEAR FELLOW, IT'S HALF PAST TEN! WHENEVER *ARE* YOU GOING TO COME? THEY LEFT YOU THE MESSAGE BECAUSE THEY COULD NOT WAIT.

WHAT MESSAGE?

GREAT ELEPHANTS! YOU ARE NOT AT ALL YOURSELF THIS MORNING. IF YOU HAD DUSTED THE MANTLEPIECE, YOU WOULD HAVE FOUND *THIS* JUST UNDER THE CLOCK.

Thorin and Company to Burglar Bilbo greetings! For your offer of professional assistance our grateful acceptance. Terms: cash on delivery up to and not exceeding one fourteenth of total profits (if any); all traveling expenses guaranteed in any event; funeral expenses to be defrayed by us or our representatives, if occasion arises.

We have proceeded in advance to make requisite preparations, and shall await your respected person at the Green Dragon Inn, Bywater, at 11:00 A.M. sharp.

We have the honor to remain yours deeply—
Thorin & Company

THAT LEAVES YOU JUST EN MINUTES. YOU WILL HAVE TO RUN.

BUT—

NO TIME FOR IT.

BUT—

NO TIME FOR THAT EITHER!

OFF YOU GO!

15

YOU'VE ET A VILLAGE AND A HALF BETWEEN YER, SINCE WE COME DOWN FROM THE MOUNTAINS. HOW MUCH MORE D'YER WANT?

OW!

A really first-class burglar would at this point have picked the trolls' pockets — it is nearly always worthwhile, if you can manage it. Others would perhaps have stuck a dagger into each of them before they observed it. Then the night could have been spent cheerily.

AND TIME'S BEEN UP OUR WAY, WHEN YER'D HAVE SAID *THANK YER BILL,* FOR A NICE BIT O' FAT VALLEY MUTTON LIKE WHAT THIS IS.

Bilbo knew it. He had read of a good many things he had never seen or done. He wished himself a hundred miles away, and yet— and yet somehow he could not go straight back to Thorin and Company empty-handed.

'ERE, 'OO ARE YOU?

Oh!

BLIMEY, BERT, LOOK WHAT I'VE COPPED!

WHAT IS IT?

LUMME, IF I KNOWS!

BILBO! WHAT...

BALIN!

A DWARF! AN *UNCOOKED* DWARF!

A SACK, TOM, QUICK!

THERE'S MORE TO COME YET, OR I'M MIGHTY MISTOOK. LOTS AND NONE AT ALL, IT IS. NO BURRAHOBBITS, BUT LOTS OF THESE HERE *DWARVES!*

I RECKON YOU'RE RIGHT AND WE'D BEST GET OUT OF THE LIGHT.

OIN? GLOIN?

And so they did. As each dwarf came up and looked at the fire, and the spilled jugs, and the gnawed mutton, in surprise, pop! went a nasty smelly sack over his head, and he was down.

THAT'LL TEACH 'EM.

WHAT'S ALL THIS TROUBLE? WHO HAS BEEN KNOCKING MY PEOPLE ABOUT?

IT'S *TROLLS!* THEY'RE HIDING IN THE BUSHES WITH SACKS.

O! ARE THEY?

19

ARRRRRRR

PSSSH

THAT LAST ONE 'URT ME IN ME EYE.

SO WE ROAST 'EM NOW! THEN WE CARRY 'EM OFF TO EAT LATER!

DON'T START THE ARGUING ALL OVER AGAIN OR IT *WILL* TAKE ALL NIGHT.

NO GOOD ROASTING 'EM NOW, IT'D TAKE ALL NIGHT.

WHO'S A-ARGUING?

YOU ARE.

YOU'RE A LIAR.

AND YOU'RE A BOOBY.

WHY DON'T WE MINCE 'EM FINE AND BOIL 'EM?

NO GOOD BOILING 'EM! WE AIN'T GOT NO WATER, AND IT'S A LONG WAY TO THE WELL AND ALL.

SHUT UP! OR WE'LL NEVER HAVE DONE. AND YER CAN FETCH THE WATER YERSELF, IF YER SAY ANY MORE.

SHUT UP YER-SELF!

WHO'S ARGUING BUT *YOU*, I'D LIKE TO KNOW.

HERE ARE SOME TROLL-PRINTS LEADING BACK THROUGH THE TREES!

PERHAPS THEIR CAVE LIES AT THE END.

They followed the tracks up the hill, until they came on a big door of stone leading to a cave. But they could not open it, not though they all pushed, while Gandalf tried various incantations.

WOULD THIS BE ANY GOOD? I FOUND IT ON THE GROUND WHERE THE TROLLS HAD THEIR FIGHT.

WHY ON EARTH DIDN'T YOU MENTION IT BEFORE?

NOW TO SEE WHAT TREASURE A TROLL HOARDS.

THIS PLACE SMELLS OF TROLLS.

AND NO WONDER.

CARRY THE GOLD OUTSIDE. WE'LL BURY IT FOR OUR RETURN TRIP.

TAKE ANY FOOD THAT HASN'T ROTTED.

22

THESE LOOK LIKE GOOD BLADES.

THEY WERE NOT MADE BY ANY TROLL, NOR ANY SMITH AMONG MEN IN THESE PARTS AND DAYS.

BUT WHEN WE CAN READ THE RUNES ON THEM, WE SHALL KNOW MORE ABOUT THEM.

WHERE DID YOU GO TO, GANDALF, IF I MAY ASK?

I WENT TO SPY OUT OUR ROAD WHEN I MET A COUPLE OF FRIENDS OF MINE FROM RIVENDELL.

IT WAS THEY WHO TOLD ME THAT THREE TROLLS HAD COME DOWN FROM THE MOUNTAINS AND SETTLED IN THE WOODS NOT FAR FROM THE ROAD.

I IMMEDIATELY HAD A FEELING THAT I WAS WANTED BACK. PLEASE BE MORE CAREFUL, NEXT TIME, OR WE SHALL NEVER GET ANYWHERE!

THANK YOU!

They did not sing or tell stories that day, nor the next day, nor the day after. They had begun to feel that danger was not far away on either side.

IS THAT *THE* MOUNTAIN?

OF COURSE NOT! THAT IS ONLY THE *BEGINNING* OF THE MISTY MOUNTAINS—

AND IT IS A GOOD WAY EVEN FROM THE *OTHER* SIDE OF THEM TO THE LONELY MOUNTAIN IN THE EAST WHERE SMAUG LIES ON OUR TREASURES.

WE MUST NOT MISS THE ROAD, OR WE SHALL BE DONE FOR!

HIDDEN SOMEWHERE AHEAD OF US IS THE FAIR VALLEY OF RIVENDELL WHERE ELROND LIVES IN THE LAST HOMELY HOUSE.

I SENT A MESSAGE BY MY FRIENDS, AND WE ARE EXPECTED.

THIS, THORIN, THE RUNES NAME ORCRIST, THE GOBLIN-CLEAVER IN THE ANCIENT TONGUE OF GONDOLIN; IT WAS A FAMOUS BLADE.

THIS, WAS GANDALF, GLAMDRING, FOE-HAMMER THAT THE KING OF GONDOLIN ONCE WORE.

KEEP THEM WELL!

I WILL KEEP THIS SWORD IN HONOUR, MAY IT SOON CLEAVE GOBLINS ONCE AGAIN!

A WISH THAT IS LIKELY TO BE GRANTED SOON ENOUGH IN THE MOUNTAINS! BUT SHOW ME NOW YOUR MAP!

WHAT IS THIS?

THERE ARE MOON-LETTERS HERE, BESIDE THE PLAIN RUNES WHICH SAY "FIVE FEET HIGH THE DOOR AND THREE MAY WALK ABREAST."

WHAT ARE MOON-LETTERS?

MOON-LETTERS ARE RUNE-LETTERS, BUT THEY CAN ONLY BE SEEN WHEN THE MOON SHINES BEHIND THEM, AND WHAT IS MORE, WITH THE MORE CUNNING SORT IT MUST BE A MOON OF THE SAME SHAPE AND SEASON AS THE DAY WHEN THEY WERE WRITTEN.

"STAND BY THE GREY STONE WHEN THE THRUSH KNOCKS AND THE SETTING SUN WITH THE LAST LIGHT OF DURIN'S DAY WILL SHINE UPON THE KEY-HOLE."

'DURIN, DURIN! HE WAS THE FATHER OF THE FATHERS OF THE ELDEST RACE OF DWARVES, THE LONGBEARDS, AND MY FIRST ANCESTOR.' I AM HIS HEIR.

THEN WHAT IS DURIN'S DAY?

WE STILL CALL IT DURIN'S DAY WHEN THE LAST MOON OF AUTUMN AND THE SUN ARE IN THE SKY TOGETHER. BUT I FEAR IT PASSES OUR SKILL IN THESE DAYS TO GUESS WHEN SUCH A TIME WILL COME AGAIN.

THESE MUST HAVE BEEN WRITTEN ON A MID-SUMMER'S EVE IN A CRESCENT MOON, A LONG WHILE AGO.

THAT REMAINS TO BE SEEN.

The next morning was a mid-summer's morning as fair and fresh as could be dreamed: blue sky and never a cloud, and the sun dancing on the water.

Now they rode away amid songs of farewell and good speed, with their hearts ready for more adventure, and with a knowledge of the road they must follow over the Misty Mountains to the land beyond.

27

There were many paths that led up into those mountains, and many passes over them. But most of the paths were cheats and deceptions and led nowhere or to bad ends; and most of the passes were infested by evil things and dreadful dangers.

The dwarves and the hobbit, helped by the wise advice of Elrond and the knowledge and memory of Gandalf, took the right road to the right pass.

YOU SEEM DOWN IN SPIRITS, BILBO.

Long days after they had climbed out of the valley and left the Last Homely House miles behind, they were still going up and up and up.

Far, far away in the West, Bilbo knew there lay his own country of safe and comfortable things, and his little hobbit hole. But it was getting bitter cold up here, and the wind came shrill among the rocks.

THE SUMMER IS GETTING ON DOWN BELOW, AND HAYMAKING IS GOING ON AND PICNICS.

THEY WILL BE HARVESTING AND BLACKBERRYING, BEFORE WE EVEN *BEGIN* TO GO DOWN THE OTHER SIDE AT THIS RATE.

andalf only shook his head and said nothing. He knew how evil and danger had grown and thriven in the Wild, since the dragons had driven men from the lands, and the goblins had spread in secret after the battle of the Mines of Moria.

He hardly dared to hope that they would pass without fearful adventure over those great tall mountains with lonely peaks and valleys where no king ruled.

They did not.

All was well, until one day they met a thunderstorm — more than a thunderstorm, a thunder-battle.

Lightning splintered on the peaks, and rocks shivered, and great crashes split the air and rolled and tumbled into every cave and hollow; and the darkness was filled with overwhelming noise and sudden light.

Bilbo had never seen or imagined anything of the kind.

OH, DEAR!

In the lightning-flashes, he saw that across the valley the stone-giants were out.

They were hurling rocks at one another for a game, and catching them, and tossing them down into the darkness where they smashed among the trees far below, or splintered into little bits with a bang.

Then came a wind and a rain, and the wind whipped the rain and the hail about in every direction. Soon they were getting drenched and their ponies were whinnying with fright.

They could hear the giants guffawing and shouting all over the mountainsides.

THIS WON'T DO AT ALL!

IF WE DON'T GET BLOWN OFF OR DROWNED, OR STRUCK BY LIGHTNING, WE SHALL BE PICKED UP BY SOME GIANT AND KICKED SKY-HIGH FOR A FOOTBALL.

THORIN! WE HAVE FOUND A DRY CAVE NOT FAR ROUND THE NEXT CORNER; AND PONIES AND ALL COULD GET INSIDE.

HAVE YOU *THOROUGHLY* EXPLORED IT?

YES, YES! IT ISN'T ALL THAT BIG, AND IT DOES NOT GO FAR BACK.

GOOD ENOUGH. LET US HAVE A LOOK AT THIS CAVE, THEN.

THE FLOOR IS DRY AND IT IS OUT OF THE RAIN.

IT WILL DO — BUT NO FIRES! WE SHALL HAVE TO GET BY WITH A CHANGE INTO DRY CLOTHES.

So they spread out their wet things on the floor and then they made their blankets comfortable.

They talked and talked, and forgot about the storm, and discussed what each would do with his share of the treasure when they got it, which at the moment did not seem so impossible).

And so they dropped off to sleep one by one.

And that was the last time that they used the ponies, packages, and paraphernalia that they had brought with them.

It turned out a good thing that night that they had brought little Bilbo with them, after all. For somehow, he could not go to sleep for a long while; and when he did sleep, he had very nasty dreams.

NEEEEEEE... KYK

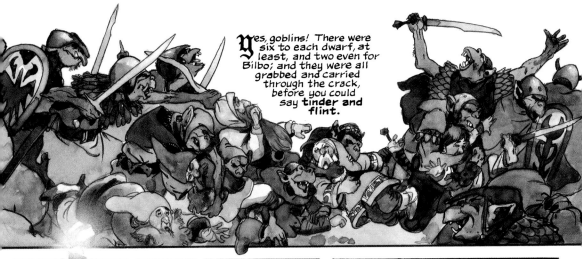

Yes, goblins! There were six to each dwarf, at least, and two even for Bilbo; and they were all grabbed and carried through the crack, before you could say **tinder and flint.**

But not Gandalf.

VROOOM

Bilbo's yell had done that much good.

But the crack closed with a snap, and Bilbo and the dwarves were on the wrong side of it!

Now goblins are cruel, wicked, and bad-hearted. They make no beautiful things, but they make many clever ones.

Hammers, axes, swords, daggers, pickaxes, tongs, and also instruments of torture, they make very well.

It is not unlikely that they invented some of the machines that have since troubled the world, especially the ingenious devices for killing large numbers of people at once.

SWSH

SMAK

THORIN THE DWARF AT YOUR SERVICE!

WE SHELTERED FROM A STORM IN WHAT SEEMED A CONVENIENT CAVE AND UNUSED; NOTHING WAS FURTHER FROM OUR THOUGHTS THAN INCONVENIENCING GOBLINS IN ANY WAY WHATEVER.

UM! SO YOU *SAY!*

MIGHT I ASK WHAT YOU WERE DOING UP IN THE MOUNTAINS AT ALL, AND WHERE YOU WERE COMING FROM, AND WHERE YOU WERE GOING TO?

IN FACT I SHOULD LIKE TO KNOW ALL ABOUT YOU, *THORIN OAKENSHIELD!*

I KNOW TOO MUCH ABOUT YOUR FOLK ALREADY; BUT LET'S HAVE THE TRUTH, OR I WILL PREPARE SOMETHING PARTICULARLY UNCOMFORTABLE FOR YOU!

WE WERE ON A JOURNEY TO VISIT OUR RELATIVES WHO LIVE ON THE EAST SIDE OF THESE TRULY HOSPITABLE MOUNTAINS.

HE IS A *LIAR,* O TRULY TREMENDOUS ONE!

SEVERAL OF OUR PEOPLE WERE STRUCK BY LIGHTNING IN THE CAVE, WHEN WE *INVITED* THESE CREATURES TO COME BELOW; AND THEY ARE AS DEAD AS STONES.

ALSO HE HAS NOT EXPLAINED *THIS!*

ORCRIST! THE GOBLIN-CLEAVER! BITER!

THE *THRICE* CURSED SWORD OF THE ELVES OF *GONDOLIN!*

MURDERS AND ELF-FRIENDS!

OH, DEAR

SCHRANNG

WE ARE DOOMED!

THE FOE-HAMMER! BEATER!

GLAM-DRING!

WE ARE LOST!

FOLLOW ME QUICK!

QUICKER, QUICKER! THE TORCHES WILL SOON BE RELIT.

HALF A MINUTE!

MISTER BAGGINS, IT SEEMS YOU LAG BEHIND.

MY STRIDE IS NOT AS GREAT AS YOURS AND THE OTHERS.

HURRY AND CLIMB ON.

WE CANNOT LEAVE OUR BURGLAR BEHIND THIS LATE IN THE GAME.

On they went.

Gandalf was quite right: they began to hear goblin noises and horrible cries far behind in the passages they had come through. That sent them on faster than ever.

And as poor Bilbo could not possibly go half as fast as the dwarves, they took it in turn to carry him on their backs.

WHY, O WHY DID I EVER LEAVE MY HOBBIT-HOLE!

WHY, O WHY DID I EVER BRING A WRETCHED LITTLE HOBBIT ON A TREASURE HUNT!

Still goblins go faster than dwarves, and soon they could hear the flap of the goblin feet, many many feet which seemed only just round the last corner.

ABOUT TURN! DRAW YOUR SWORD, THORIN!

URK!

BITER!

BEATER!

BITER AND BEATER!

FLEE!

It was quite a long while before any goblins dared turn that corner. By that time the dwarves had gone on again, a long, long, way on into the dark tunnels of the goblins' realm.

When the goblins discovered that, they put out their torches and they slipped on soft shoes, and they chose out their very quickest runners with the sharpest ears and eyes. These ran forward, as swift as weasels in the dark, and with hardly any more noise than bats.

That is why neither Bilbo, nor the dwarves, nor even Gandalf heard them coming.

OH!

DORI!

SOME-BODY!

OW!

OW!

OW!

OW!

UH!

When Bilbo opened his eyes, he wondered if he had; for it was just as dark as with them shut. No one was anywhere near him. Just imagine his fright!
GANDALF?
THORIN?
DORI?
It was then that Bilbo's hand met a cold metal object in the dark.
HUH?
A RING?
NO TIME TO LOOK AT IT NOW. I'VE GOT TO FIND A WAY OUT OF THIS TERRIBLE PLACE.
It was a turning point in his career, but he did not know it.
WHERE ARE THE OTHERS?
AM I THE ONLY ONE LEFT?
AT LEAST I STILL HAVE MY PIPE.
IF ONLY I CAN FIND SOME MATCH—
HMM? WHAT'S THIS?
MY TROLL SWORD! SO IT IS AN ELVISH BLADE TOO.
AND FROM ITS GLOW I SEE GOBLINS ARE NOT VERY NEAR, AND YET NOT FAR ENOUGH.

GO BACK? NO GOOD AT ALL! GO SIDEWAYS? IMPOSSIBLE! GO FORWARD?

ONLY THING TO DO! ON WE GO!

The tunnel seemed to have no end. All Bilbo knew was that it was still going down pretty steadily and keeping in the same direction. There were passages leading off to the side every now and then. Of these he took no notice, except to hurry past for fear of goblins.

I do not know how long he kept on like this, hating to go on, not daring to stop, on, on, until he was tireder than tired. It seemed like all the way to tomorrow and over it to the days beyond.

UGH!

SPLOSH

I DON'T HEAR THE SOUND OF RUNNING WATER. SO IT IS A POOL OR A LAKE, AND NOT AN UNDERGROUND RIVER I'VE FOUND. AND IT'S PROBABLY FULL OF SLIMY THINGS, WITH BIG BULGING BLIND EYES, WRIGGLING IN THE WATER.

NOW WHICH WAY DO I GO?

There are strange things living in the pools and lakes in the hearts of mountains: fish whose fathers swam in, goodness only knows how many years ago, and never swam out again; also there are other things more slimy than fish.

Even in the tunnels and caves the goblins have made for themselves there are other things living unbeknown to them that have sneaked in from outside to lie up in the dark.

Deep down here by the dark water lived old Gollum.

42

WHAT'S HE GOT IN HIS HANDSES?

A SWORD, A BLADE WHICH CAME OUT OF GONDOLIN!

SSSS

PRAPS YE SITS HERE AND CHATS WITH IT A BITSY, MY PRECIOUSSS.

IT LIKES RIDDLES, PRAPS IT DOES, DOES IT?

Gollum was anxious to appear friendly, and riddles was all he could think of. Asking them had been the only game he had ever played, sitting in his hole in the long, long ago, before he crept down into the dark under the mountains.

VERY WELL.

YOU ASK FIRST.

WHAT HAS ROOTS AS NOBODY SEES, IS TALLER THAN TREES, UP, UP IT GOES AND YET NEVER GROWS?

EASY! MOUNTAIN, I SUPPOSE.

DOES IT GUESS EASY? IT MUST HAVE A COMPETITION WITH US, MY PRECIOUSS! IF IT ASKS US, AND WE DOESN'T ANSWER, THEN WE DOES WHAT IT WANTS, EH? WE SHOWS IT THE WAY OUT, YES!

IF PRECIOUS ASKS, AND IT DOESN'T ANSWER, WE *EATS* IT. gollum!

To be continued—

DAVID WENZEL

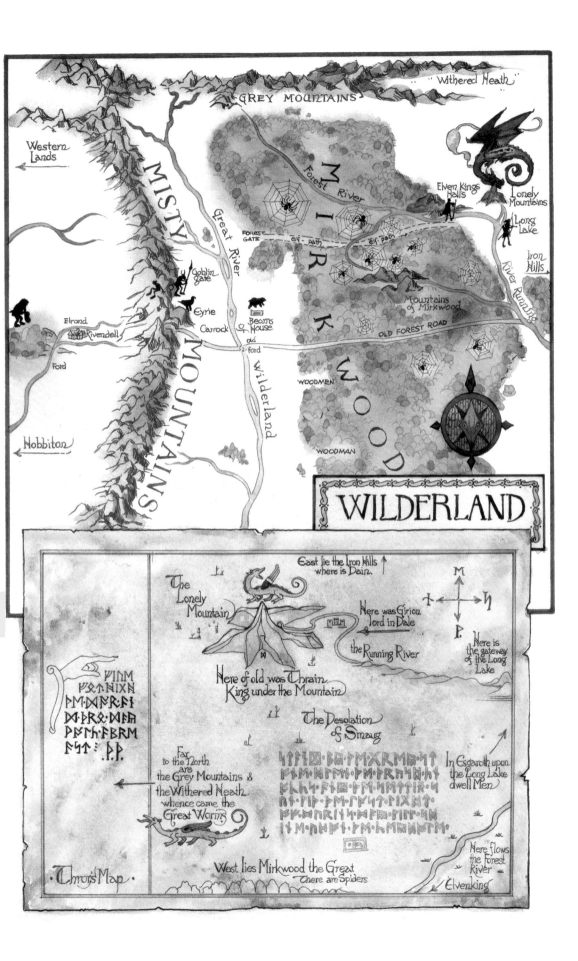

OTHER GREAT BOOKS FROM ECLIPSE

SABRE
BY DON McGREGOR
AND PAUL GULACY
(1978) 48PP, 8 1/2 x 11, B&W
$6.95 TRADE PAPERBACK
$25.95 CLOTHBOUND SIGNED LIMITED
EDITION

THE ROCKETEER
BY DAVE STEVENS
(1985) 72PP, 8 1/2 x 11, FULL COLOUR
$8.95 TRADE PAPERBACK $29.95 CLOTHBOUND

THE SACRED AND THE PROFANE
BY KEN STEACY AND DEAN MOTTER
(1987) 128PP, 8 1/2 x 11, FULL COLOUR
$15.95 TRADE PAPERBACK $25.95 CLOTHBOUND
$36.00 CLOTHBOUND SIGNED LIMITED EDITION

SOMERSET HOLMES
BY BRUCE JONES, APRIL CAMPBELL,
AND BRENT ANDERSON
(1987) 128PP, 8 1/2 x 11, FULL COLOUR
$15.95 TRADE PAPERBACK $25.95 CLOTHBOUND
$36.00 CLOTHBOUND SIGNED LIMITED EDITION

SILVERHEELS
BY BRUCE JONES, SCOTT HAMPTON,
AND APRIL CAMPBELL
(1987) 64PP, 8 1/2 x 11, FULL COLOUR
$8.95 TRADE PAPERBACK
$25.00 HARDBOUND SIGNED LIMITED EDITION

VALKYRIE, PRISONER OF THE PAST
BY CHARLES DIXON, PAUL GULACY AND WILL BLYBERG
(1988) 76PP, 7 x 10, FULL COLOUR
$7.95 TRADE PAPERBACK
$30.95 CLOTHBOUND SIGNED LIMITED EDITION

SCOUT: THE FOUR MONSTERS
BY TIMOTHY TRUMAN AND THOMAS YEATES
(1988) 136PP, 7 x 10, FULL COLOUR
$15.95 TRADE PAPERBACK
$36.00 CLOTHBOUND SIGNED LIMITED EDITION

BROUGHT TO LIGHT
BY ALAN MOORE, BILL SIENKIEWICZ, JOYCE BRABNER,
THOMAS YEATES, AND PAUL MAVRIDES
(1988) 80PP, 8 1/2 x 11, FULL COLOUR
$9.95 TRADE PAPERBACK $30.95 CLOTHBOUND

ALEX TOTH'S ZORRO Vol. 1 & 2
(1988) 120PP, 8 1/2 x 11, B&W
$10.95 EACH, TRADE PAPERBACK
$55.00 CLOTHBOUND VOLS 1 AND 2 SIGNED LIMITED
EDITION, TOGETHER IN ONE SLIPCASE

BOGIE
BY CLAUDE JEAN-PHILIPPE AND PATRICK LESUEUR
(1988) 64PP, 8 1/2 x 11, FULL COLOUR
$10.95 TRADE PAPERBACK

**TEENAGED DOPE SLAVES AND REFORM
SCHOOL GIRLS**
EDITED BY DEAN MULLANEY
(1988) 112PP, 8 1/2 x 11, B&W
$10.95 TRADE PAPERBACK

MIRACLEMAN: BOOK ONE
BY ALAN MOORE, GARRY LEACH, AND ALAN DAVIS
(1988) 80PP, 7 x 10, FULL COLOUR
$10.95 TRADE PAPERBACK $30.95 CLOTHBOUND

HEARTBREAK COMICS
BY DAVID BOSWELL
(1988) 48PP, 8 1/2 x 11, B&W
$5.95 TRADE PAPERBACK

**REAL LOVE: THE BEST OF THE SIMON & KIRBY
ROMANCE COMICS**
EDITED BY RICHARD HOWELL
(1988) 160PP, 8 1/2 x 11, B&W
$13.95 TRADE PAPERBACK

**PIGEONS FROM HELL BY ROBERT E.
HOWARD**
ADAPTED BY SCOTT HAMPTON
(1988) 64PP, 8 1/2 x 11, FULL COLOUR
$8.95 TRADE PAPERBACK
$30.95 CLOTHBOUND SIGNED LIMITED EDITION

**ARIANE & BLUEBEARD BY MAURICE
MAETERLINCK**
ADAPTED BY P. CRAIG RUSSELL
(1988) 48PP, 7 x 10, FULL COLOUR
$4.95 TRADE PAPERBACK
$30.95 CLOTHBOUND SIGNED LIMITED EDITION

INTO THE SHADOW OF THE SUN: RAEL
BY COLIN WILSON
(1988) 48PP, 8 1/2 x 11, FULL COLOUR
$8.95 TRADE PAPERBACK

**DR. WATCHSTOP: ADVENTURES IN TIME
AND SPACE**
BY KEN MACKLIN
(1989) 64PP, 8 1/2 x 11, FULL COLOUR
$8.95 TRADE PAPERBACK
$30.95 CLOTHBOUND SIGNED LIMITED EDITION

**JAMES BOND 007: PERMISSION TO DIE
Vol. 1-3**
BY MIKE GRELL
(1989) 48PP, 7 x 10, FULL COLOUR
$4.95 EACH, TRADE PAPERBACK

JAMES BOND 007: LICENCE TO KILL
BY MIKE GRELL, RICHARD ASHFORD, CHUCK AUSTEN,
TOM YEATES AND STAN WOCH
(1989) 48PP, 8 1/2 x 11, FULL COLOUR
$8.95 TRADE PAPERBACK $30.95 CLOTHBOUND

**TAPPING THE VEIN Vol. 1 & 2 BY CLIVE
BARKER**
ADAPTED BY P. CRAIG RUSSELL , SCOTT HAMPTON,
JOHN BOLTON AND KLAUS JANSON
(1989) 64PP, 7 x 10, FULL COLOUR
$7.95 EACH, TRADE PAPERBACK

TOADSWART D'AMPLESTONE
BY TIM CONRAD
(1989) 112PP, 8 1/2 x 11, B&W
$9.95 TRADE PAPERBACK
$36.00 CLOTHBOUND SIGNED LIMITED EDITION

For a complete list of available books, trading cards, and comics with postpaid prices,
send a self-addressed stamped envelope to:
Eclipse Books, P. O. Box 1099, Forestville, California 95436